ANTONIO VIVALDI

FLUTE CONCERTOS
CONCERTOS POUR FLUTE

JANET SEE
PHILHARMONIA BAROQUE ORCHESTRA
dir. NICHOLAS McGEGAN

+ **CATALOGUE** harmonia mundi **1993**

ANTONIO VIVALDI
(1678-1741)
Flute Concertos/Concertos pour flûte

JANET SEE, *flute*
* Stephen Schultz, *second flute*
PHILHARMONIA BAROQUE ORCHESTRA
dir. NICHOLAS McGEGAN

Vivaldi's fifteen concertos for transverse flute may have been among the last of his concertos. In his first years (from 1703) at the Ospedale della Pietà in Venice his responsibilities were connected entirely with providing music for strings and teaching his female charges to play violins, violas, and cellos to a standard that suited his increasingly virtuoso style of performance.

Transverse flutes, which flourished in many German courts, were still uncommon in Northern Italy when Quantz toured in 1726. Since Vivaldi was a priest and the Pietà a religious institution, it would most probably not have been acceptable to teach the recorder there. This did not prevent Vivaldi from writting six concertos for recorder (three each for alto and sopranino tunings), but it may have heightenned his interest in the transverse flute, when he finally became acquainted with it, since it was viewed as acceptable for use in the sacred repertory. Ignazio Siber, a highly regarded oboist, was engaged to teach "traversier" at the Pietà in 1728. Vivaldi's first dated use of the instrument occurred in his opera *Orlando,* which was performed in Venice in November 1727.

Modern editions of Vivaldi's music have sometimes muted the differences between the recorder and the flute. Beside the fact that they had different symbolic connotations, they also had divergent technical properties that suited them to different tonalities and kinds of passagework. Multiple copies of a few individual works indicate that Vivaldi considered the difference sufficiently important to warrant transposition and reworking in recycling apparently earlier pieces with recorder for the flute. All of the pieces in this recording were originally created for the transverse flute. Only the celebrated "Gardellino" (Goldfinch) concerto was published ; it appeared as No. 3 of Op. 10 (1728), which was the first volume of concertos for the medium ever published. In a curious way, Vivaldi approaches the flute with the same textural ambivalence as he had the violin more than fifteen years earlier in his first violin concertos, those of Op. 3. That is to say, he sometimes treats it as a true soloist and sometimes pairs it with another instrument (a violin in RV 429 ; a second flute in RV 533). An interesting variation on the second procedure is that of coupling the flute with an obbligato cello (as happens in RV 428 and 438). The first movement of the latter work is, in fact, also used in the cello concerto RV 414 ; a variant of the former is scored for flute and oboe.

ELEANOR SELFRIDGE-FIELD

Les quinze concertos pour flûte traversière de Vivaldi font peut-être partie des dernières œuvres du genre qu'il ait composées. Durant ses premières années (cela dès 1703) à l'Ospedale della Pietà à Venise, il avait surtout pour fonction de fournir des partitions pour cordes et d'enseigner aux jeunes filles confiées à sa tutelle le violon, l'alto et le violoncelle et leur faire atteindre un niveau d'exécution de plus en plus conforme à la virtuosité qu'il imposait.

La flûte traversière, en usage dans plusieurs cours allemandes, n'était pas encore répandue en Italie du Nord lorsque Quantz y fit sa tournée en 1726. Vivaldi étant prêtre et la Pietà une institution religieuse, l'enseignement de la flûte à bec n'aurait pu y être admis. Vivaldi n'en composa pas moins de six concertos pour flûte à bec (trois pour l'alto et trois pour la sopranino). Cette situation semble avoir relevé son intérêt à l'égard de la flûte traversière qui devint pour lui un instrument d'autant plus familier qu'il était admis dans le répertoire religieux. En 1728, Ignazio Siber, hautboïste de renom, fut engagé pour enseigner la « traversière » à la Pietà. Pour la première fois dans l'œuvre vivaldienne, cet instrument fut intégré à l'opéra *Orlando* joué à Venise en novembre 1727.

Les versions récentes des œuvres de Vivaldi ont quelquefois passé sous silence les différences entre flûte traversière et flûte à bec. A part les différentes connotations symboliques qu'ils représentent, les deux instruments possèdent également des caractéristiques techniques qui les prédisposent à des tonalités et des traitements différents. Si l'on en juge les nombreuses copies de certaines œuvres, Vivaldi considérait ces différences suffisamment importantes pour justifier la transposition et l'adaptation, afin que des pièces apparemmment plus anciennes destinées à la flûte à bec puissent être jouées à la flûte traversière.

Toutes les œuvres constituant cet enregistrement furent à l'origine composées pour flûte traversière. Seul le célèbre concerto « Gardellino » (le chardonneret doré) fut publié ; il porte le n° 3 de l'op. 10 de 1728 qui constitue le premier volume jamais édité de concertos pour cet instrument. Curieusement, Vivaldi traite la flûte avec la même ambivalence que lorsqu'il avait composé ses premiers concertos pour violon (op. 3) plus de quinze ans auparavant : elle joue tantôt en véritable soliste, tantôt en duo avec un autre instrument (un violon dans le RV 429, une seconde flûte dans le RV 533). Une variante intéressante de cette dernière technique apparaît dans la combinaison flûte/violoncelle obligé (comme dans les RV 428 et 438). Le premier mouvement de cette dernière œuvre est d'ailleurs également utilisé dans le concerto RV 414 pour violoncelle ; une autre version du concerto RV 428 a été écrite pour flûte et hautbois.

Vivaldis fünfzehn Konzerte für Querflöte gehören wahrscheinlich seiner späten Schaffensperiode an. Während der ersten Jahre (ab 1703) am *Ospedale della Pietà* in Venedig legte ihm sein Amt vor allem auf, Musik für Streichinstrumente zu komponieren und seinen Violine-, Viola- und Cello-Schülerinnen seinen zunehmend virtuosen Vortragsstil zu übermitteln.

Die an deutschen Höfen sehr beliebte Querflöte war in Norditalien, als Quantz 1726 dorthin reiste, immer noch ungewöhnlich.

Da Vivaldi Priester war und die *Pietà* eine religiöse Institution, stand es außer Frage, dort Flötenunterricht zu erteilen. Das hinderte Vivaldi aber nicht, sechs Blockflöten-Konzerte (drei für Sopran- und drei für Altblockflöte) zu schreiben und erhöhte wahrscheinlich sein Interesse für die Querflöte, als er dieses Instrument kennenlernte, zudem es in der Kirchenmusik akzeptiert war. Ignazio Siber, ein hochgeachteter Oboist, wurde 1728 an der *Pietà* angestellt, um "Traversier" zu unterrichten. Vivaldis ersten nachgewiesenen Gebrauch der Querflöte finden wir in seiner 1727 in Venedig uraufgeführten Oper *Orlando*.

Moderne Ausgaben von Vivaldis Werken haben oft den Unterschied zwischen Blockflöte und Querflöte verwischt. Abgesehen von ihrer unterschiedlichen symbolischen Zugehörigkeit bestimmen sie ihre technischen Charakteristiken für verschiedene Klangfarben und Arpeggien. Zahlreiche Kopien einiger Einzelwerke bezeugen, daß Vivaldi diesem Unterschied genügend Wichtigkeit beimaß, transponierte und überarbeitete er doch selbst ursprünglich für Blockflöte geschriebene Werke für die Querflöte.

Alle Werke dieser Aufnahme sind Originalwerke für Querflöte. Nur das berühmte Konzert "Il Gardellino" (der Distelfink) ist als Nr. 3 des Opus 10 (1728) im Druck erschienen. Es war die erste gedruckte Sammlung für Flöte überhaupt. Auf eigenartige Weise behandelt Vivaldi die Flöte mit derselben strukturellen Ambivalenz wie 15 Jahre früher die Violine in seinen ersten Violinkonzerten des Opus 3; d.h., daß die Flöte teils als echtes Soloinstrument eingesetzt, teils mit anderen Instrumenten gepaart wird. (Eine Violine in RV 429, eine zweite Flöte in RV 533.) Eine interessante Variante dieses zweiten Verfahrens ist das Zusammenspiel von Flöte und obligatem Cello in RV 428 und 438. Den ersten Satz des letzteren Werkes sollte Vivaldi in der Tat noch einmal in seinem Cello-Konzert RV 414 verwenden. Es besteht davon eine Variante für Flöte und Oboe.

COMPOSITEURS
COMPOSERS
KOMPONISTEN

HENRICO ALBICASTRO
Cantate, Sonates & Concertos
Guy de Mey • Ensemble 415, Chiara Banchini
CD HMC 905208 - MC HMC 405208

FRANCISCO ANTÓNIO DE ALMEIDA
La Giuditta, oratorio
Concerto Köln, dir. René Jacobs
2 CD HMC 901411.12

CARL PHILIPP EMANUEL BACH
Sonates pour viole de gambe et clavecin
London Baroque, Charles Medlam
CD HMC 901410 - MC HMC 401410

JOHANN SEBASTIAN BACH
Die Kunst der Fuge, BWV 1080
Davitt Moroney, clavecin John Phillips
2 CD HMC 901169.70

JOHANN SEBASTIAN BACH
Das wohltemperierte Clavier, BWV 846-893
Davitt Moroney, clavecin John Phillips
4 CD HMC 901285.88

JOHANN SEBASTIAN BACH
"Trauer-Ode" BWV 198 • **Cantate** BWV 78
La Chapelle Royale, dir. Philippe Herreweghe
CD HMC 901270 – MC HMC 401270

JOHANN SEBASTIAN BACH
Cantates BWV 21 & BWV 42
La Chapelle Royale, Collegium Vocale, Herreweghe
CD HMC 901328 – MC HMC 401328

JOHANN SEBASTIAN BACH
Cantates pour alto BWV 35, 82 & 53
René Jacobs • Ensemble 415, Chiara Banchini
CD HMC 901273 – MC HMC 401273

JOHANN SEBASTIAN BACH
Cantates pour basse BWV 82, 56 & 158
Peter Kooy • Dir. Philippe Herreweghe
CD HMC 901365 - MC HMC 401365

JOHANN SEBASTIAN BACH
Klavierbüchlein für Anna Magdalena Bach
Lorraine Hunt, soprano • Nicholas McGegan
CD HMU 907042 - MC HMU 407042

JOHANN SEBASTIAN BACH
Magnificat BWV 243 • **Cantate** BWV 80
La Chapelle Royale, Collegium Vocale, Herreweghe
CD HMC 901326 – MC HMC 401326

JOHANN SEBASTIAN BACH
Motets BWV 225-231
La Chapelle Royale, Collegium Vocale, Herreweghe
CD HMC 901231 – 2 MC HMC 401231.32

JOHANN SEBASTIAN BACH
Musikalisches Opfer, BWV 1079
Moroney, See, Holloway, ter Linden, Cook
CD HMC 901260 – MC HMC 401260

JOHANN SEBASTIAN BACH
Johannes-Passion, BWV 245
La Chapelle Royale, Collegium Vocale, Herreweghe
2 CD HMC 901264.65 – 2 MC HMC 401264.65

JOHANN SEBASTIAN BACH
Matthäus-Passion, BWV 244
La Chapelle Royale, Collegium Vocale, Herreweghe
3 CD HMC 901155.57 – 3 MC HMC 401155.57

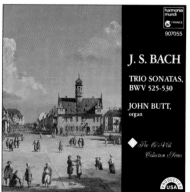

JOHANN SEBASTIAN BACH
Intégrale des Sonates en trio
John Butt, orgue Greg Harrold, Hertz Hall
CD HMU 907055 - MC HMU 407055

JOHANN SEBASTIAN BACH
Sonates en Trio BWV 1037-39, 1079
London Baroque, Charles Medlam
CD HMC 901173 – MC HMC 401173

JOHANN SEBASTIAN BACH
Intégrale des Sonates pour flûte et clavecin
Janet See, flûte • Davitt Moroney, clavecin
2 CD HMC 907024.25 – 2 MC HMU 407024.25

JOHANN SEBASTIAN BACH
Sonates pour flûte et clavecin BWV 1030/35
Marc Beaucoudray, flûte • William Christie, clavecin
CD HMC 90065

JOHANN SEBASTIAN BACH
Suites de clavecin BWV 1006a, 818a, 819a, 997
Emer Buckley, clavecin von Nagel
CD HMC 901300 – MC HMC 401300

JOHANN SEBASTIAN BACH
Suites pour flûte à bec seule
Marion Verbruggen
CD HMU 907071 - MC HMU 407071

JOHANN SEBASTIAN BACH
Variations Goldberg, BWV 988
Kenneth Gilbert, clavecin Hubert Bédard
CD HMC 901240

ADRIANO BANCHIERI • LUCA MARENZIO
Barca di Venetia per Padova • Madrigaux
Ensemble Clément Janequin
CD HMC 901281 – MC HMC 401281

LUDWIG VAN BEETHOVEN
Christus am Ölberge, op.85
Ch. & Orch. National de Lyon, dir. Serge Baudo
CD HMC 905181 – MC HMC 405181

LUDWIG VAN BEETHOVEN
Sonate op.110, Variations op.76
Brigitte Engerer, piano
CD HMC 901346

LUDWIG VAN BEETHOVEN
Sonates pour piano et violoncelle op.5
Ch. Coin, violoncelle • P. Cohen, pianoforte
CD HMC 901179

LUDWIG VAN BEETHOVEN
Sonate pour piano et violoncelle, op.69
Ch. Coin, violoncelle • P. Cohen, pianoforte
CD HMC 901180

LUDWIG VAN BEETHOVEN
Trios op.1 n° 1 & 2
Patrick Cohen • Erich Höbarth • Christophe Coin
CD HMC 901361 - MC HMC 401361

LUDWIG VAN BEETHOVEN/FRANZ LISZT
Symphonie n° 3 "Eroica"
Georges Pludermacher, piano
CD HMC 901193

LUDWIG VAN BEETHOVEN/FRANZ LISZT
Symphonie n° 6 "Pastorale"
Michel Dalberto, piano
CD HMC 901196

LUDWIG VAN BEETHOVEN/FRANZ LISZT
Symphonie n° 9 en ré mineur
Alain Planès, Georges Pludermacher, pianos
CD HMC 901198 – MC HMC 401198

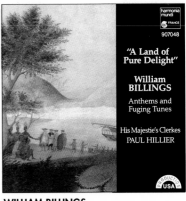

WILLIAM BILLINGS
Anthems and Fuging Tunes
His Majestie's Clerkes, Paul Hillier
CD HMU 907048 - MC HMU 407048

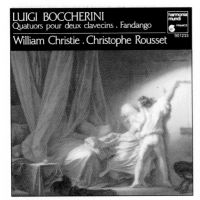

LUIGI BOCCHERINI
Quatuors pour deux clavecins • Fandango
William Christie • Christophe Rousset
CD HMC 901233

LUIGI BOCCHERINI
Quintettes avec contrebasse op.39
Ensemble 415, Chiara Banchini
CD HMC 901334 – MC HMC 401334

LUIGI BOCCHERINI
Quintettes avec deux altos op.60/1 & 5, op.62/1
Ensemble 415, Chiara Banchini
CD HMC 901402

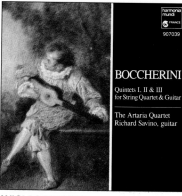

LUIGI BOCCHERINI
Quintettes pour guitare et cordes n°1, 2 & 3
Richard Savino, guitare • The Artaria Quartet
CD HMU 907039 - MC HMU 407039

LUIGI BOCCHERINI
Quintettes pour guitare et cordes n° 4, 5 & 6
Richard Savino, guitare • The Artaria Quartet
CD HMU 907026 – MC HMU 407026

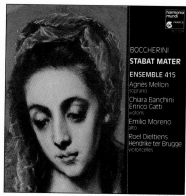

LUIGI BOCCHERINI
Stabat Mater (Version originale 1781)
A. Mellon, soprano • Ensemble 415, Chiara Banchini
CD HMC 901378 - MC HMC 401378

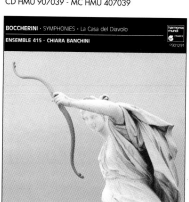

LUIGI BOCCHERINI
Symphonies ("La casa del Diavolo", etc)
Ensemble 415, dir. Chiara Banchini
CD HMC 901291 – MC HMC 401291

JOHANNES BRAHMS
Motets, op.109, 29, 74 & 110
La Chapelle Royale, Collegium Vocale, Herreweghe
CD HMC 901122 – MC HMC 401122

JOHANNES BRAHMS
Quatuor avec piano op.25 n°1 • Sonate op.108
J.-C. Pennetier, R. Pasquier, B. Pasquier, R. Pidoux
CD HMC 901062 – MC HMC 401062

JOHANNES BRAHMS
Quintettes op.111 & 115
Gérard Caussé, Michel Portal • Melos Quartett
CD HMC 901349 – MC HMC 401349

JOHANNES BRAHMS
Sextuor à cordes n°1 • Trio n° 3, op.101
Les Musiciens
CD HMC 901073

JOHANNES BRAHMS
Sonates pour clarinette et piano, op.120
Michel Portal • Georges Pludermacher
CD HMC 90904

BRAHMS • Trio op.40 • BEETHOVEN, VON KRUFFT • Sonates pour cor & piano
L. Greer, cor • S. Chase, violon • S. Lubin, pianoforte
CD HMU 907037 - MC HMU 407037

MAX BRUCH • 8 Pièces op.83 ALEXANDER VON ZEMLINSKY • Trio op.3
Ensemble Walter Boeykens
CD HMC 901371 - MC HMC 401371

ANTON BRUCKNER
Messe en mi mineur • Motets
Dir. Philippe Herreweghe
CD HMC 901322 – MC HMC 401322

ANTON BRUCKNER
Quintette à cordes
Melos Quartett, Enrique Santiago (alto)
CD HMC 901421

DIETRICH BUXTEHUDE
Membra Jesu Nostri, BuxWV 75
Concerto Vocale, dir. René Jacobs
CD HMC 901333 – MC HMC 401333

WILLIAM BYRD
Messes & Motets
Chanticleer
CD HMU 905182 – MC HMU 405182

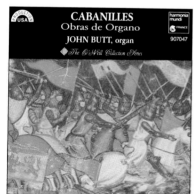

JUAN CABANILLES
Obras de Organo
John Butt, orgue Greg Harrold
CD HMU 907047 - MC HMU 407047

THOMAS CAMPION
Ayres
Drew Minter, contre-ténor • Paul O'Dette, luth
CD HMU 907023 – MC HMU 407023

ANDRÉ CAMPRA
Idoménée (opéra)
Les Arts Florissants, dir. William Christie
3 CD HMC 901396.98 - 3 MC HMC 401396.98

ANDRÉ CAMPRA
Messe de Requiem
La Chapelle Royale, dir. Philippe Herreweghe
CD HMC 901251 – MC HMC 401251

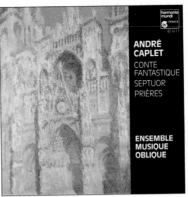

ANDRÉ CAPLET
Conte fantastique • Prières • Septuor
Laurence Cabel, harpe • Ens. Musique Oblique
CD HMC 901417

FRANCESCO CAVALLI
Giasone, opéra en 3 actes
Concerto Vocale, dir. René Jacobs
3 CD HMC 901282.84 – 3 MC HMC 401282.84

FRANCESCO CAVALLI
Xerse, opéra en 3 actes
Concerto Vocale, dir. René Jacobs
4 CD HMC 901175.78 – 4 MC HMC 401175.78

PIETRO ANTONIO CESTI
Orontea, opéra en 3 actes
Concerto Vocale, dir. René Jacobs
3 CD HMC 901100.02

MARC-ANTOINE CHARPENTIER
David et Jonathas
Les Arts Florissants, dir. William Christie
2 CD HMC 901289.90 – 2 MC HMC 401289.90

MARC-ANTOINE CHARPENTIER
Leçons de Ténèbres du Mercredy Sainct
Concerto Vocale, dir. René Jacobs
CD HMC 901005

MARC-ANTOINE CHARPENTIER
Leçons de Ténèbres du Jeudy Sainct
Concerto Vocale, dir. René Jacobs
CD HMC 901006

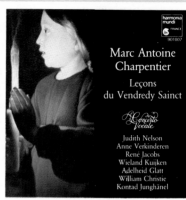

MARC-ANTOINE CHARPENTIER
Leçons de Ténèbres du Vendredy Sainct
Concerto Vocale, dir. René Jacobs
CD HMC 901007

MARC-ANTOINE CHARPENTIER/MOLIÈRE
Le Malade imaginaire, H.495
Les Arts Florissants, dir. William Christie
CD HMC 901336 – MC HMC 401336

MARC-ANTOINE CHARPENTIER
Médée, opéra en 5 actes
Les Arts Florissants, dir. William Christie
3 CD HMC 901139.41

MARC-ANTOINE CHARPENTIER
Motets • Miserere H.219
La Chapelle Royale, dir. Philippe Herreweghe
CD HMC 901185 – MC HMC 401185

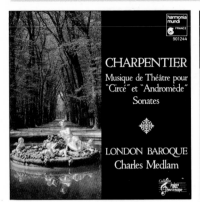

MARC-ANTOINE CHARPENTIER
Musique de Théâtre • Sonate à huit • Concert
London Baroque, dir. Charles Medlam
CD HMC 901244

MARC-ANTOINE CHARPENTIER
Un Oratorio de Noël • Pastorale H.482
Les Arts Florissants, dir. William Christie
CD HMC 905130

MARC-ANTOINE CHARPENTIER
Caecilia, Virgo et Martyr • Filius Prodigus
Les Arts Florissants, dir. William Christie
CD HMC 90066

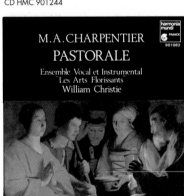

MARC-ANTOINE CHARPENTIER
Pastorale sur la Naissance de N.S. Jésus-Christ
Les Arts Florissants, dir. William Christie
CD HMC 901082

MARC-ANTOINE CHARPENTIER
Te Deum • Missa Assumpta est Maria
Les Arts Florissants, dir. William Christie
CD HMC 901298 – MC HMC 401298

FREDERIC CHOPIN • RICHARD STRAUSS
Sonates pour violoncelle et piano
Lluís Claret, violoncelle • Alain Planès, piano
CD HMC 901370 - MC HMC 401370

LOUIS-NICOLAS CLÉRAMBAULT
Pyrame et Tisbé • La Muse de l'Opéra • Orphée
Les Arts Florissants, dir. William Christie
CD HMC 901329 – MC HMC 401329

ARCANGELO CORELLI
Concerti grossi op. 6
Ens. 415, dir Chiara Banchini & Jesper Christensen
2 CD HMC 901406.07 - 2 MC HMC 401406.07

ARCANGELO CORELLI
Concerti grossi op. 6 n° 1 à 6
Philharmonia Baroque Orchestra, dir. N.McGegan
CD HMU 907014 – MC HMU 407014

ARCANGELO CORELLI
Concerti grossi op. 6 n° 7 à 12
Philharmonia Baroque Orchestra, dir. N.McGegan
CD HMU 907015 – MC HMU 407015

ARCANGELO CORELLI
Sonate da chiesa op. 1 & 3
London Baroque, Charles Medlam
2 CD HMC 901344.45 – MC HMC 401344 & HMC 401345

ARCANGELO CORELLI
Sonate da camera op. 2 & 4
London Baroque, Charles Medlam
2 CD HMC 901342.43 – MC HMC 401342 & HMC 401343

ARCANGELO CORELLI
Sonate a Violino e Violone o Cimbalo, op. 5 / 1
Ensemble 415, Chiara Banchini
CD HMC 901307

JOHANNES CORNAGO
Missa de la mapa mundi • Secular Music
The Newberry Consort, Hillier, Springfels
CD HMU 907083

FRANÇOIS COUPERIN
L'Apothéose de Lully • Pièces à deux clavecins
William Christie, Christophe Rousset
CD HMC 901269 – MC HMC 401269

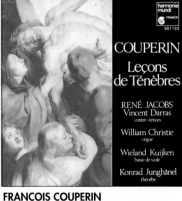

FRANÇOIS COUPERIN
Leçons de Ténèbres
Concerto Vocale, dir. René Jacobs
CD HMC 901133 – MC HMC 401133

MICHEL-RICHARD DELALANDE
Dies Irae, S.31 • Miserere, S.27
La Chapelle Royale, dir. Philippe Herreweghe
CD HMC 901352 – MC HMC 401352

MICHEL-RICHARD DELALANDE
Petits Motets
Les Arts Florissants, dir. William Christie
CD HMC 901416 - MC HMC 401416

MICHEL-RICHARD DELALANDE
Symphonies pour les Soupers du Roy
La Simphonie du Marais, dir. Hugo Reyne
4 CD HMC 901337.40 • CD HMC 901303 (extraits)

MICHEL-RICHARD DELALANDE
Te Deum • Grands Motets
Les Arts Florissants, dir. William Christie
CD HMC 901351 – MC HMC 401351

JOSQUIN DESPREZ
Adieu mes amours • Chansons
Ens. Clément Janequin • Ens. Les Eléments
CD HMC 901279 – MC HMC 401279

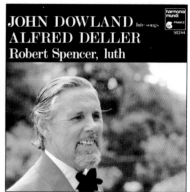

JOSQUIN DESPREZ
Missa Pange Lingua
Ens. Clément Janequin • Ens. Organum
CD HMC 901239

JOSQUIN DESPREZ
Stabat Mater dolorosa / Motets
La Chapelle Royale, dir. Philippe Herreweghe
CD HMC 901243 – MC HMC 401243

JOHN DOWLAND
Lute Songs, Lute Solos – Vol. I
A. Deller, haute-contre • The Consort of Six
CD HMC 90244

JOHN DOWLAND · LUTE SONGS Vol. II · Come, heavy sleep
ALFRED DELLER · ROBERT SPENCER, luth
harmonia mundi FRANCE 90245

JOHN DOWLAND
Lute Songs, Lute Solos – Vol. II
A. Deller, haute-contre • The Consort of Six
CD HMC 90245

DVOŘÁK
TRIOS op. 65 & 90

TRIO DE BARCELONA
Albert G. Attenelle
Gerard Claret
Lluis Claret
harmonia mundi FRANCE 901404

ANTONIN DVORAK
Trios op.65 & 90 "Dumky"
Trio de Barcelona
CD HMC 901404 - MC HMC 401404

DE FALLA • EL AMOR BRUJO
EL RETABLO DE MAESE PEDRO
Orquestra de Cambra Teatre Lliure de Barcelona
dir. JOSEP PONS
harmonia mundi FRANCE 905213

MANUEL DE FALLA
El Amor brujo • El Retablo de Maese Pedro
Orquestra de Cambra Teatre Lliure, dir. J. Pons
CD HMC 905213 - MC HMC 405213

FALLA · SIETE CANCIONES POPULARES ESPAÑOLAS
CONCERTO · EL GRAN TEATRO DEL MUNDO
Victoria de los Angeles
Orquestra de Cambra Teatre Lliure, dir. Josep Pons
harmonia mundi FRANCE 901432

MANUEL DE FALLA
Siete canciones populares españolas • Concerto
Victoria de los Angeles • O.C.T.L., dir. J. Pons
CD HMC 901432 - MC HMC 401432

FAURÉ · REQUIEM version 1893
LA CHAPELLE ROYALE · ENSEMBLE MUSIQUE OBLIQUE
PHILIPPE HERREWEGHE
harmonia mundi FRANCE 901292

GABRIEL FAURÉ
Messe de Requiem, op.48
A. Mellon, P. Kooy • Dir. Philippe Herreweghe
CD HMC 901292 – MC HMC 401292

J.J. FROBERGER
SUITES & TOCCATAS
CHRISTOPHE ROUSSET
harmonia mundi FRANCE 901572

JOHANN JAKOB FROBERGER
Suites • Toccatas • Tombeau • Lamentation
Christophe Rousset, clavecin Couchet (1652)
CD HMC 901372 - MC HMC 401372

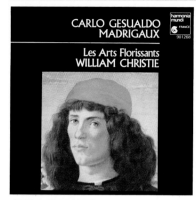

CARLO GESUALDO
Madrigaux à 5 voix
Les Arts Florissants, dir. William Christie
CD HMC 901268 – MC HMC 401268

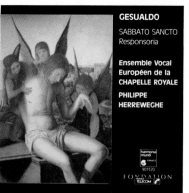

CARLO GESUALDO
Sabbato Sancto, répons du Samedi Saint
E.V.E. La Chapelle Royale, dir. P. Herreweghe
CD HMC 901320 – MC HMC 401320

JEAN GILLES
Requiem • Diligam te, Domine
La Chapelle Royale, dir. Philippe Herreweghe
CD HMC 901341 – MC HMC 401341

CHRISTOPH WILLIBALD GLUCK
Echo et Narcisse
Concerto Köln, dir. René Jacobs
2 CD HMC 905201.02 – 2 MC HMC 405201.02

GEORG FRIEDRICH HAENDEL
Aci, Galatea e Polifemo
London Baroque, dir. Charles Medlam
2 CD HMC 901253.54 – 2 MC HMC 401253.54

GEORG FRIEDRICH HAENDEL
Arias for Cuzzoni (extraits d'opéras)
L. Saffer • Philharmonia Baroque Orch., McGegan
CD HMU 907036 – MC HMU 407036

GEORG FRIEDRICH HAENDEL
Intégrale des sonates pour flûte à bec
Hugo Reyne, flûte • J. Hantaï, P. Monteilhet, P. Hantaï
CD HMC 905211 - MC HMC 405211

GEORG FRIEDRICH HAENDEL
Suites de clavecin n° 2, 3, 5, 6 & 7
Kenneth Gilbert, clavecin Hubert Bédard
CD HMC 90447

GEORG FRIEDRICH HAENDEL
Tirsi, Clori e Fileno, pastorale
Philharmonia Baroque Orchestra, dir. N.McGegan
CD HMU 907045 - MC HMU 407045

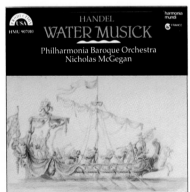

GEORG FRIEDRICH HAENDEL
Water Musick
Philharmonia Baroque Orchestra, dir. N.McGegan
CD HMU 907010 – MC HMU 407010

GEORG FRIEDRICH HAENDEL
Messiah
Philharmonia Baroque Orchestra, dir. N.McGegan
3 CD HMU 907050.52 – 3 MC HMU 407050.52

GEORG FRIEDRICH HAENDEL
La Resurrezione, oratorio
Philharmonia Baroque Orchestra, dir. N.McGegan
2 CD HMU 907027.28 – 2 MC HMU 407027.28

GEORG FRIEDRICH HAENDEL
Arias for Durastanti (extraits d'opéras)
L. Hunt • Philharmonia Baroque Orch., McGegan
CD HMU 907056

GEORG FRIEDRICH HAENDEL
Arias for Montagnana (extraits d'opéras)
D. Thomas • Philharmonia Baroque Orch., McGegan
CD HMU 907016 – MC HMU 407016

GEORG FRIEDRICH HAENDEL
Arias for Senesino (extraits d'opéras)
D. Minter • Philharmonia Baroque Orch., McGegan
CD HMU 905183 – MC HMU 405183

GEORG FRIEDRICH HAENDEL
Apollo e Dafne • Concerto pour hautbois
Philharmonia Baroque Orchestra, dir. N. McGegan
CD HMU 905157

GEORG FRIEDRICH HAENDEL
Sonates en trio, op.2
London Baroque
CD HMC 901379 - MC HMC 401379

GEORG FRIEDRICH HAENDEL
Sonates pour deux violons et basse continue
London Baroque
CD HMC 901389 - MC HMC 401389

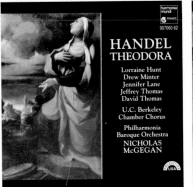

GEORG FRIEDRICH HAENDEL
Theodora, oratorio
Philharmonia Baroque Orchestra, dir. N.McGegan
3 CD HMU 907060.62 - 3 MC HMU 407060.62

GEORG FRIEDRICH HAENDEL
Susanna, oratorio
Philharmonia Baroque Orchestra, dir. N.McGegan
3 CD HMU 907030.32 – 3 MC HMU 407030.32

GEORG FRIEDRICH HAENDEL
Agrippina, opéra
Capella Savaria, dir. Nicholas McGegan
3 CD HMU 907063.65 - 3 MC HMU 407063.65

GEORG FRIEDRICH HAENDEL
Flavio, opéra
Ens. 415 / Chiara Banchini, dir. René Jacobs
2 CD HMC 901312.13 – 2 MC HMC 401312.13

GEORG FRIEDRICH HAENDEL
Giulio Cesare, opéra
Concerto Köln, dir. René Jacobs
3 CD HMC 901385.87 - 3 MC HMC 401385.87

GEORG FRIEDRICH HAENDEL
Ottone, opéra
Philharmonia Baroque Orchestra, dir. N.McGegan
3 CD HMU 907073.75

HANS LEO HASSLER
Missa "Super Dixit Maria" • Motets
E.V.E. La Chapelle Royale, dir. P. Herreweghe
CD HMC 901401

JOSEPH HAYDN
Trios avec pianoforte, Hob. XV: 12, 13 & 14
Patrick Cohen • Erich Höbarth • Christophe Coin
CD HMC 901277

JOSEPH HAYDN
Trios avec pianoforte, Hob. XV: 18, 19 & 20
Patrick Cohen • Erich Höbarth • Christophe Coin
CD HMC 901314 • MC HMC 901314

JOSEPH HAYDN
Trios avec pianoforte, Hob. XV: 21, 22 & 23
Patrick Cohen • Erich Höbarth • Christophe Coin
CD HMC 901400

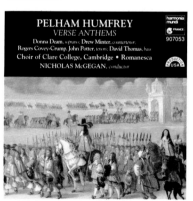

PELHAM HUMFREY
Verse Anthems
Choir of Clare College • Romanesca • N. McGegan
CD HMU 907053

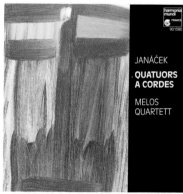

LEOŠ JANÁČEK
Quatuors "Sonate à Kreutzer" & "Lettres intimes"
Melos Quartett
CD HMC 901380 - MC HMC 401380

**LEOŠ JANÁČEK • "Mládí" • Concertino
ANTONIN DVOŘÁK • Sérénade op. 44**
Ensemble Walter Boeykens
CD HMC 901399 - MC HMC 401399

**CLÉMENT JANEQUIN
Le Chant des Oyseaulx • Chansons**
Ensemble Clément Janequin
CD HMC 901099 – MC HMC 401099

**CLÉMENT JANEQUIN
La Chasse • Chansons**
Ensemble Clément Janequin
CD HMC 901271 – MC HMC 401271

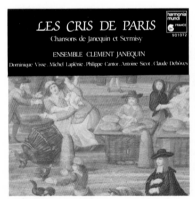

**CLÉMENT JANEQUIN • Les Cris de Paris
CLAUDIN DE SERMISY • Chansons**
Ensemble Clément Janequin
CD HMC 901072 – MC HMC 401072

**GIOVANNI GIROLAMO KAPSBERGER
"Il Tedesco della Tiorba" • Pièces pour luth**
Paul O'Dette, luth
CD HMU 907020 – MC HMU 407020

**ZOLTÁN KODÁLY
Sonates pour violoncelle** op. 4 & 8
L. Claret, violoncelle • R.-M. Cabestany, piano
CD HMC 901325 – MC HMC 401325

KROMMER • HOFFMEISTER
Concertos pour deux clarinettes
A. & W. Boeykens, Het Nieuw Belgisch Kamerorkest
CD HMC 901433

JOHANN KUHNAU
Frische Clavier Früchte (Sonates pour clavecin)
John Butt, clavecin
CD HMU 907097

PIERRE DE LA RUE
Missa "L'Homme armé" • Requiem
Ensemble Clément Janequin
CD HMC 901296

ROLAND DE LASSUS
Chansons & Moresche
Ensemble Clément Janequin
CD HMC 901391 - MC HMC 401391

ROLAND DE LASSUS
Hieremiae Prophetae Lamentationes
E.V.E. La Chapelle Royale, dir. P. Herreweghe
CD HMC 901299 – MC HMC 401299

WILLIAM LAWES
Fantasia-suites pour deux violons et continuo
London Baroque, Charles Medlam
CD HMC 901423

JEAN-BAPTISTE LULLY
Atys, opéra en 5 actes
Les Arts Florissants, dir. William Christie
3 CD HMC 901257.59 – 3 MC HMC 401257.59

JEAN-BAPTISTE LULLY
Atys (extraits)
Les Arts Florissants, dir. William Christie
CD HMC 901249 – MC HMC 401249

JEAN-BAPTISTE LULLY • Dies Irae/Miserere
HENRY DUMONT • Memorare
La Chapelle Royale, dir. Philippe Herreweghe
CD HMC 901167

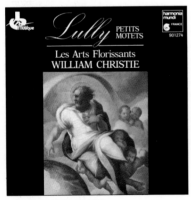

JEAN-BAPTISTE LULLY
Petits Motets
Les Arts Florissants, dir. William Christie
CD HMC 901274

MARIN MARAIS • Suites pour viole
Sonnerie de Ste Geneviève du Mont
Nikolaus Harnoncourt, viole de gambe
CD HMC 90414

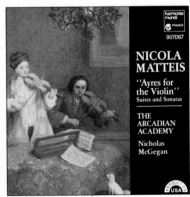

NICOLA MATTEIS
Ayres for the violin (Suites & Sonatas)
The Arcadian Academy • Nicholas McGegan
CD HMU 907067 - MC HMU 407067

DOMENICO MAZZOCCHI
Sacrae Concertationes
Nederlands Kamerkoor, dir. René Jacobs
CD HMC 901357 – MC HMC 4013573

FELIX MENDELSSOHN
Psaumes op. 42 & 31 • **Ave Maria,** op. 23 n° 2
Eiddwen Harry • Dir. Philippe Herreweghe
CD HMC 901272

FELIX MENDELSSOHN
Trios avec piano op. 49 & 66
Trio de Barcelona
CD HMC 901335 – MC HMC 401335

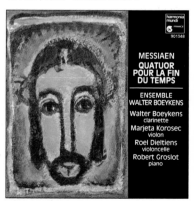

OLIVIER MESSIAEN
Quatuor pour la fin du temps
Ensemble Walter Boeykens
CD HMC 901348 – MC HMC 401348

MICHEL PIGNOLET DE MONTECLAIR
Cantates • La Mort de Didon, etc
Les Arts Florissants, dir. William Christie
CD HMC 901280

MICHEL PIGNOLET DE MONTECLAIR
Jephté, opéra
Les Arts Florissants, dir. William Christie
2 CD HMC 901424.25

CLAUDIO MONTEVERDI
Il Ballo delle Ingrate • Sestina
Les Arts Florissants, dir. William Christie
CD HMC 901108

CLAUDIO MONTEVERDI
Il ritorno d'Ulisse in patria, opéra
Concerto Vocale, dir. René Jacobs
3 CD HMC 901427.29

CLAUDIO MONTEVERDI
L'incoronazione di Poppea, opéra
Concerto Vocale, dir. René Jacobs
3 CD HMC 901330.32 – 3 MC HMC 401330.32

CLAUDIO MONTEVERDI
Lamento d'Arianna • Madrigaux
H. Müller-Molinari, R. Jacobs • Concerto Vocale
CD HMC 901129 – MC HMC 401129

CLAUDIO MONTEVERDI
Missa in illo tempore • Messa a quattro voci
E.V.E. La Chapelle Royale, dir. P. Herreweghe
CD HMC 901355 - MC HMC 401355

CLAUDIO MONTEVERDI
Selva morale e spirituale (extraits)
Les Arts Florissants, dir. William Christie
CD HMC 901250 – MC HMC 401250

CLAUDIO MONTEVERDI
Vespro della Beata Vergine
La Chapelle Royale, Collegium Vocale, Herreweghe
2 CD HMC 901247.48 – MC HMC 401247.48

MODESTE MOUSSORGSKI
Tableaux d'une Exposition
Brigitte Engerer, piano
CD HMC 901266 – MC HMC 401266

WOLFGANG AMADEUS MOZART
Concerto pour clarinette • Symphonies
M. Portal • Wiener Kammerorchester, P. Entremont
CD HMC 901304 – MC HMC 401304

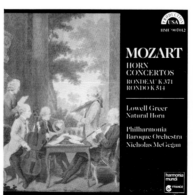

W. A. MOZART • Concertos K.107
J.C. BACH • Concerto/Sonate
London Baroque, Charles Medlam
CD HMC 901395 - MC HMC 401395

WOLFGANG AMADEUS MOZART
Concertos pour cor, K. 412, 417, 447, 495
Lowell Greer, cor naturel • Dir. N. McGegan
CD HMU 907012 – MC HMU 407012

W. A. MOZART • Divertimenti K. 439 b
ANTON STADLER • Trios pour cors de basset
The New World Basset Horn Trio
CD HMU 907017 – MC HMU 407017

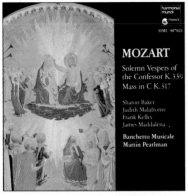

WOLFGANG AMADEUS MOZART
Messe du Couronnement/Vêpres solennelles
Banchetto Musicale, dir. Martin Pearlman
CD HMU 907021 – MC HMU 407021

WOLFGANG AMADEUS MOZART
Messe en ut mineur K.427
Dir. Philippe Herreweghe
CD HMC 901393 - MC HMC 401393

WOLFGANG AMADEUS MOZART
Quatuor K.421 • Quintette K.516
Quatuor Ysaÿe (Hatto Beyerle, 2e alto)
CD HMC 905203

WOLFGANG AMADEUS MOZART
Quatuors pour piano et cordes K.478 & K.493
The Mozartean Players • Steven Lubin, pianoforte
CD HMU 907018 – MC HMU 407018

WOLFGANG AMADEUS MOZART
Quintette avec clarinette/Kegelstatt-Trio
Michel Portal, clarinette • Les Musiciens
CD HMC 901118 – MC HMC 401118

WOLFGANG AMADEUS MOZART
Quintette avec clarinette/Kegelstatt-Trio
Ensemble Walter Boeykens
CD HMC 901384 - MC HMC 401384

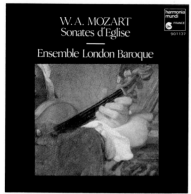

WOLFGANG AMADEUS MOZART
Sonates d'église
London Baroque, dir. Charles Medlam
CD HMC 901137

WOLFGANG AMADEUS MOZART
Intégrale des Sonates pour piano
Georges Pludermacher, piano
5 CD HMC 901373.77

WOLFGANG AMADEUS MOZART
Intégrale des Trios avec pianoforte
The Mozartean Players
2 CD HMU 907033.34 - 2 MC HMU 407033.34

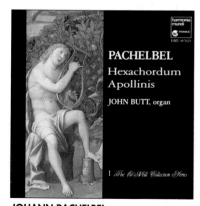

JOHANN PACHELBEL
Hexachordum Apollinis
John Butt, orgue Greg Harrold, Hertz Hall
CD HMU 907029 – MC HMU 407029

N. PAGANINI • Caprices n° 2, 5, 9, 18, etc
P. SARASATE • Carmen-Fantaisie, Habanera
Tedi Papavrami, violon • Christophe Larrieu, piano
CD HMC 905207

GIOVANNI PIERLUIGI DA PALESTRINA
Missa & Motet Viri Galilaei
E.V.E La Chapelle Royale • Ensemble Organum
CD HMC 901388 - MC HMC 401388

FRANCIS POULENC
Stabat Mater • Litanies à la Vierge noire
Ch. et Orch. National de Lyon, dir. Serge Baudo
CD HMC 905149 – MC HMC 405149

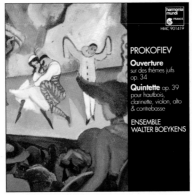

SERGE PROKOFIEV
Quintette op.39 • Ouverture op.34
Ensemble Walter Boeykens
CD HMC 901419

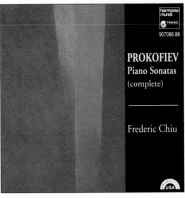

SERGE PROKOFIEV
Intégrale des Sonates pour piano (n° 1 à 9)
Frederic Chiu, piano
3 CD HMU 907086.88

HENRY PURCELL • Chamber music
Sonates • Pavanes • Ouvertures • Chaconne
London Baroque, dir. Charles Medlam
CD HMC 901327 – MC HMC 401327

HENRY PURCELL
Chansons de tavernes et de chapelles
Deller Consort, dir. Alfred Deller
CD HMC 90242 – MC HMC 40242

HENRY PURCELL
Dido & Aeneas
Les Arts Florissants, dir. William Christie
CD HMC 905173 – MC HMC 405173

HENRY PURCELL
The Fairy Queen
Les Arts Florissants, dir. William Christie
2 CD HMC 901308.09 – 2 MC HMC 401308.09

HENRY PURCELL
The Indian Queen
Deller Consort, The King's Musick, Alfred Deller
CD HMC 90243

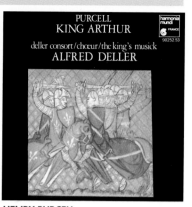

HENRY PURCELL
King Arthur • Timon of Athens
Deller Consort, The King's Musick, Alfred Deller
2 CD HMC 90252.53 – 2 MC HMC 40252.53

HENRY PURCELL
Music for a while • The Plaint • O solitude
Alfred Deller • Wieland Kuijken • William Christie
CD HMC 90249 – MC HMC 40249

HENRY PURCELL
"Sweeter than roses" and other songs
D. Minter • P. O'Dette • M. Meyerson • M. Springfels
CD HMU 907035

HENRY PURCELL
Ten Sonata's in Four Parts
London Baroque, Charles Medlam
CD HMC 901438

SERGE RACHMANINOV • Œuvre pour deux pianos / piano à quatre mains
Brigitte Engerer, Oleg Maisenberg, pianos
2 CD HMC 901301.02 – 2 MC HMC 401301.02

JEAN-PHILIPPE RAMEAU Grands Motets
La Chapelle Royale, dir. Philippe Herreweghe
CD HMC 901078 – MC HMC 401078

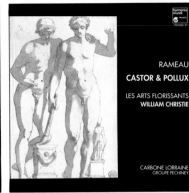

JEAN-PHILIPPE RAMEAU Castor & Pollux, opéra
Les Arts Florissants, dir. William Christie
CD HMC 901435.37

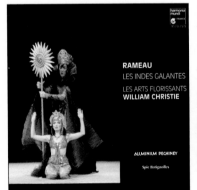

JEAN-PHILIPPE RAMEAU Les Indes galantes, opéra
Les Arts Florissants, dir. William Christie
3 CD HMC 901367.69 - 3 MC HMC 401367.69

JEAN-PHILIPPE RAMEAU Pièces de clavecin en concerts
Ch. Rousset, clavecin • R. Terakado • K. Uemura
CD HMC 901418 – MC HMC 401418

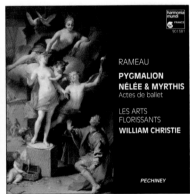

JEAN-PHILIPPE RAMEAU Pygmalion / Nélée et Myrthis
Les Arts Florissants, dir. William Christie
CD HMC 901381 - MC HMC 401381

MAURICE RAVEL
Boléro • Concertos pour piano • La valse
G. Pludermacher • O. N. Lille, dir. J.-C. Casadesus
CD HMC 901434 - MC HMC 401434

MAURICE RAVEL
L'œuvre pour violon et piano
Régis Pasquier, violon • Brigitte Engerer, piano
CD HMC 901364 - MC HMC 401364

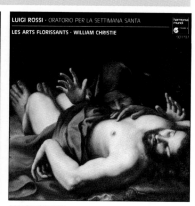

LUIGI ROSSI
Oratorio per la Settimana Santa
Les Arts Florissants, dir. William Christie
CD HMC 901297 – MC HMC 401297

LUIGI ROSSI
Orfeo, opéra
Les Arts Florissants, dir. William Christie
3 CD HMC 901358.60 – 3 MC HMC 401358.60

GIOACCHINO ROSSINI
Péchés de vieillesse (Sélection)
Frederic Chiu, piano
CD HMU 907102

DOMENICO SCARLATTI
Trente Sonates
Rafael Puyana, clavecin Hass
2 CD HMC 901164.65

JOHANN SCHOBERT
Quatuors • Trios • Sonates
L. Sgrizzi, pianoforte • Ens. 415, Chiara Banchini
CD HMC 901294 – MC HMC 401294

ARNOLD SCHOENBERG • Pierrot Lunaire
Kammersymphonie op. 9 (transcr. WEBERN)
M. Pousseur • Musique Oblique • P. Herreweghe
CD HMC 901390 - MC HMC 401390

FRANZ SCHUBERT
Les derniers quatuors, op. 29, 161* et posth.
Melos Quartett
2 CD HMC 901408.09 - MC HMC 401408*

FRANZ SCHUBERT
Octuor en Fa majeur op. 168
Music from Aston Magna, vol. 1
CD HMU 907049 - MC HMU 407049

FRANZ SCHUBERT • Sonate "Arpeggione"
FELIX MENDELSSOHN • Sonates n° 1 & 2
Lluís Claret, violoncelle • Alain Planès, piano
CD HMC 901383 - MC HMC 401383

FRANZ SCHUBERT
Sonate "Arpeggione" • Trios D. 581 & 471
Les Musiciens
CD HMC 901035 – MC HMC 401035

FRANZ SCHUBERT
Trio op.99 • Sonate pour piano op.120
J.C. Pennetier • R. Pasquier • R. Pidoux
CD HMC 901048 – MC HMC 401048

FRANZ SCHUBERT
Trio op.100
J.C. Pennetier • R. Pasquier • R. Pidoux
CD HMC 901047 – MC HMC 401047

ROBERT SCHUMANN
Sonates pour violon et piano n⁰ˢ 1 & 2
Olivier Charlier, violon • Brigitte Engerer, piano
CD HMC 901405 - MC HMC 401405

HEINRICH SCHÜTZ
Auferstehungs-Historie, SWV 50
Concerto Vocale, dir. René Jacobs
CD HMC 901311 – MC HMC 401311

HEINRICH SCHÜTZ
Kleine geistliche Konzerte
Sebastian Hennig, René Jacobs • Concerto Vocale
CD HMC 901097 – MC HMC 401097

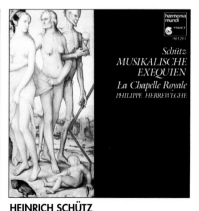

HEINRICH SCHÜTZ
Musikalische Exequien • Motets
La Chapelle Royale, dir. Philippe Herreweghe
CD HMC 901261 – MC HMC 401261

HEINRICH SCHÜTZ
Die sieben Worte Jesu Christi am Kreuz
Ens. Clément Janequin • Les Saqueboutiers de Toulouse
CD HMC 901255 – MC HMC 401255

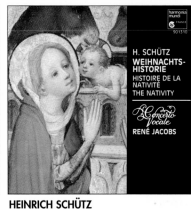

HEINRICH SCHÜTZ
Weihnachts-Historie
Concerto Vocale, dir. René Jacobs
CD HMC 901310 – MC HMC 401310

ALEXANDRE SCRIABINE
Sonates pour piano, vol. 1 (n° 3, 4, 5, 10)
Robert Taub, piano
CD HMU 907011 – MC HMU 407011

ALEXANDRE SCRIABINE
Sonates pour piano, vol. 2 (n° 1, 6, 9)
Robert Taub, piano
CD HMU 907019 – MC HMU 407019

ALEXANDRE SCRIABINE
Sonates pour piano, vol. 3 (n° 2, 7, 8)
Robert Taub, piano
CD HMU 907041 – MC HMU 407041

STRAVINSKI • Suite de L'Histoire du soldat
BARTÓK • Contrastes
Ensemble Walter Boeykens
CD HMC 901356 – MC HMC 401356

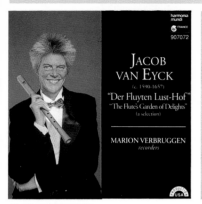

harmonia mundi FRANCE
907072

JACOB
VAN EYCK
(c. 1590-1657)
"Der Fluyten Lust-Hof"
"The Flute's Garden of Delights"
(a selection)

MARION VERBRUGGEN
recorders

JACOB VAN EYCK
Der Fluyten Lust-Hof (extraits)
Marion Verbruggen, flûtes à bec
CD HMU 907072

harmonia mundi USA
905193

Vivaldi
FLUTE CONCERTOS
Janet See, flute
Philharmonia Baroque Orchestra
Nicholas McGegan

ANTONIO VIVALDI
Concertos pour flûte
Janet See • Dir. Nicholas McGegan
CD HMU 905193 – MC HMU 405193

harmonia mundi FRANCE
907040

VIVALDI
RECORDER CONCERTOS

Marion Verbruggen

Philharmonia
Baroque Orchestra

Nicholas
McGegan

ANTONIO VIVALDI
Concertos pour flûte à bec
Marion Verbruggen • Dir. Nicholas McGegan
CD HMU 907040 - MC HMU 407040

harmonia mundi FRANCE
907046

"La Pastorella"
VIVALDI
Chamber Concertos

Marion Verbruggen
recorder
Paul Goodwin
oboe
John Holloway
violin
Dennis Godburn
bassoon
John Toll
harpsichord
Sebastian Comberti
'cello

ANTONIO VIVALDI
La Pastorella • Concertos & Sonates • Trio
Verbruggen, Goodwin, Holloway, Godburn, Toll,
Comberti – CD HMU 907046 – MC HMU 407046

harmonia mundi FRANCE
905129

Vivaldi
I quattro Stagioni
Concerto Amsterdam · Jaap Schröder

ANTONIO VIVALDI
Les Quatre Saisons
Concerto Amsterdam, dir. Jaap Schröder
CD HMC 905129

harmonia mundi FRANCE

VIVALDI
SONATE A TRE
"LA FOLLIA"
SONATE
A DUE VIOLINI

Ensemble 415
CHIARA BANCHINI
Véronique MÉJEAN
Käthi GOHL
Jesper CHRISTENSEN

ANTONIO VIVALDI
"La Follia" • Sonate a due & a tre violine
Ensemble 415, Chiara Banchini
CD HMC 901366 - MC HMC 401366

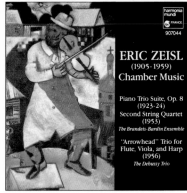

KURT WEILL
Berliner Requiem • Violinkonzert
Ens. Musique Oblique, dir. Ph. Herreweghe
CD HMC 901422

WILLIAM WALTON
Concerto pour violon • Suite "Henry V"
Aaron Rosand • Florida Phil. Orch., James Judd
CD HMU 907070

ERIC ZEISL
Chamber Music
The Brandeis-Bardin Ensemble • The Debussy Trio
CD HMU 907044 - MC HMU 407044

ANTHOLOGIES
RECITALS
SAMMELPROGRAMME

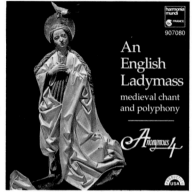

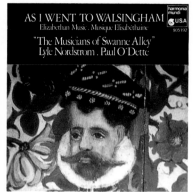

AN ENGLISH LADYMASS
Polyphonie mariale des XIIIᵉ/XIVᵉ siècles
Anonymous 4
CD HMU 907080 · MC HMU 407080

AS I WENT TO WALSINGHAM
Musique Elisabéthaine (Johnson, Byrd, Collarde, etc.)
The Musicians of Swanne Alley
CD HMU 905192 – MC HMU 405192

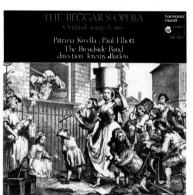

¡ AY AMOR ! • Chansons & musique de théâtre espagnoles (XVIIᵉ s.)
The Newberry Consort, dir. Mary Springfels
CD HMU 907022 – MC HMU 407022

THE BEGGAR'S OPERA
L'Opéra des Gueux
The Broadside Band, dir. Jeremy Barlow
CD HMC 901071

CARMINA BURANA
Version originale
Clemencic Consort, dir. René Clemencic
CD HMC 90335 – MC HMA 43335

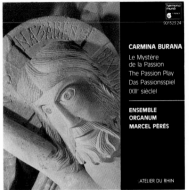

CARMINA BURANA (XIIIe siècle)
Le Grand Mystère de la Passion
Ensemble Organum, dir. Marcel Pérès
CD HMC 901323.24 – MC HMC 401323.24

CHANT BYZANTIN
Passion et Résurrection
Sœur Marie Keyrouz
CD HMC 901315 – MC HMC 401315

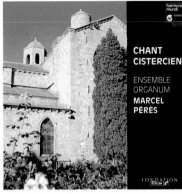

CHANT CISTERCIEN (XIIe siècle)
Répons de Matines pour la fête de Saint-Bernard
Ensemble Organum, dir. Marcel Pérès
CD HMC 901392 - MC HMC 401392

CHANTS DE L'ÉGLISE MILANAISE
Ensemble Organum
dir. Marcel Pérès
CD HMC 901295 – MC HMC 401295

CHANTS DE L'ÉGLISE DE ROME
Période Byzantine
Ensemble Organum, dir. Marcel Pérès
CD HMC 901218 – MC HMC 401218

CHANT GRÉGORIEN
Répons et monodies gallicanes
Deller Consort, dir. Alfred Deller
CD HMC 90234 – MC HMC 40234

CHANT GRÉGORIEN
pour le temps Pascal
Capella Antiqua de Munich, dir. Konrad Ruhland
CD HMC 905113

CHANT TRADITIONNEL MARONITE
Noël – Passion – Résurrection
Sœur Marie Keyrouz • "L'Ensemble de la Paix"
CD HMC 901350 – MC HMC 401350

FREDERIC CHIU
Transcriptions pour piano
Frédéric Chiu, piano
CD HMU 907054 – MC HMU 407054

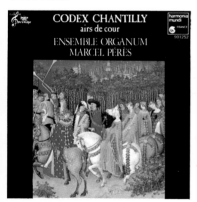

CODEX CHANTILLY
Airs de cour du XIVe siècle
Ensemble Organum, dir. Marcel Pérès
CD HMC 901252 – MC HMC 401252

CODEX FAENZA (Italie XVe siècle)
Machaut, Landini, Jacopo da Bologna, etc.
Ensemble Organum, dir. Marcel Pérès
CD HMC 901354 - MC HMC 401354

CORSICA
Chants polyphoniques
E Voce di u Cumune
CD HMC 901256 – MC HMC 401256

DANSES POPULAIRES FRANÇAISES
Orchésographie d'Arbeau (1588), etc.
The Broadside Band, dir. Jeremy Barlow
CD HMC 901152

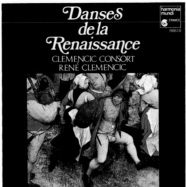

DANSES DE LA RENAISSANCE
Susato, Phalèse, Hassler, Attaingnant, etc.
Clemencic Consort, dir. René Clemencic
CD HMC 90610 – MC HMC 40610

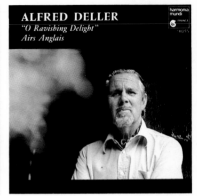

ALFRED DELLER • "O RAVISHING DELIGHT"
Airs anglais des XVIIe et XVIIIe siècles
Avec D. Munrow, R. Lee, D. Dupré, R. Elliott
CD HMC 90215

DUOS ROMANTIQUES
Mendelssohn, Liszt, Schumann, Brahms
Brigitte Fassbaender, Hidenori Komatsu, Kurt Moll
CD HMC 905210 – MC HMC 405210

FANDANGO
Gregorio Paniagua
CD HMC 901394 - MC HMC 401394

LA FÊTE DE L'ÂNE
Traditions du Moyen-Âge
Clemencic Consort, dir. René Clemencic
CD HMC 901036 – MC HMC 401036

FLÛTE À BEC, LUTH ET GUITARE
Telemann, Bach, Haendel, Dowland, Van Eyck
R.Clemencic, flûte à bec • A.Kécskès, luth, guitare
CD HMC 90427 – MC HMA 43247

LA FOLIA DE LA SPAGNIA
Réalisation a-musicologique G.Paniagua
Atrium Musicae de Madrid, dir. G. Paniagua
CD HMC 901050 – MC HMC 401050

GRADUEL D'ALIÉNOR DE BRETAGNE
Plain-chant et polyphonie des XIIIᵉ et XIVᵉ s.
Ensemble Organum, dir. Marcel Pérès
CD HMC 901403 - MC HMC 401403

RÉCITAL DE HARPE • ISABELLE MORETTI
Sonates de C.P.E. Bach, J.L. Dussek,
P. Hindemith, A. Casella, G. Tailleferre
CD HMC 905184

LE JEU DES PÈLERINS D'EMMAÜS
Drame liturgique du XIIᵉ siècle
Ensemble Organum, dir. Marcel Pérès
CD HMC 901347 – MC HMC 401347

GRANDE LITURGIE ORTHODOXE SLAVE
en la Basilique Alexandre Newsky de Sofia
Chœur Bulgare "Svetoslav Obretenov", dir. G. Robev
CD HMC 90101 – MC HMC 40101

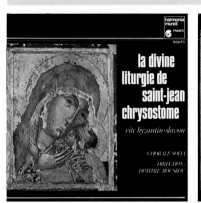

LA DIVINE LITURGIE DE SAINT-JEAN CHRYSOSTOME • Rite byzantin-slavon
Chorale Sofia, dir. Dimitre Rouskov
CD HMC 90641 – MC HMC 40641

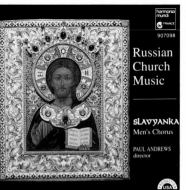

LITURGIE ORTHODOXE RUSSE
Russian Church Music
Chœur d'hommes "Slavyanka", dir. Paul Andrews
CD HMU 907098 – MC HMU 407098

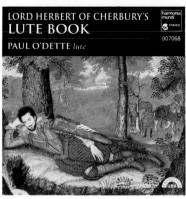

LORD HERBERT OF CHERBURY'S LUTE BOOK
Paul O'Dette, luth
CD HMU 907068

MESSE DE SAINT MARCEL
Chants de l'église de Rome (VIIᵉ-XIIIᵉ siècles)
Ensemble Organum, dir. Marcel Pérès
CD HMC 901382 - MC HMC 401382

MESSE DE TOURNAI
XIVᵉ siècle
Ensemble Organum, dir. Marcel Pérès
CD HMC 901353 – MC HMC 401353

MUSIQUE ARABO-ANDALOUSE
Atrium Musicae de Madrid
dir. Gregorio Paniagua
CD HMC 90389 – MC HMC 40389

MUSICK FOR SEVERALL FRIENDS
Chansons et sonates anglaises du XVIIe s.
The Newberry Consort, dir. Mary Springfels
CD HMU 907013 – MC HMU 407013

PLAIN-CHANT
Cathédrale d'Auxerre (XVIIIe siècle)
Ensemble Organum, dir. Marcel Pérès
CD HMC 901319 – MC HMC 401319

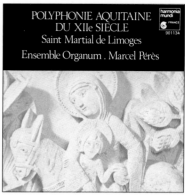

POLYPHONIE AQUITAINE DU XIIe SIÈCLE
(Saint-Martial de Limoges)
Ensemble Organum, dir. Marcel Pérès
CD HMC 901134

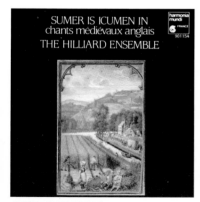

SUMER IS ICUMEN IN
Chants médiévaux anglais
The Hilliard Ensemble, dir. Paul Hillier
CD HMC 901154 – MC HMC 401154

TARENTULE-TARENTELLE
Tarentelles des XVIIe et XVIIIe siècles
Atrium Musicae de Madrid, dir. G. Paniagua
CD HMC 90379

TROUBADOURS
Peirol, B. de Ventadorn, R. de Vaqueiras
Clemencic Consort, dir. René Clemencic
CD HMC 90396

harmonia mundi s.a., Mas de Vert, 13200 Arles ℗ 1988, 1993
Production harmonia mundi U.S.A.
Enregistrement / Recording :
mars / March 1987, Lone Mountain College Chapel, San Francisco
Prise de son / Engineer : Peter McGrath
Direction artistique / Producer : Robina G. Young
Montage / Editing assistance : Hugh B. Davies
Traductions / Translations : Global Language Services
Illustration / Cover : Carel Fabritius, Le Chardonneret doré / The Goldfinch
© Mauritshuis, Den Haag
Maquette Relations, Arles

Imprimé en CEE pour le compte de harmonia mundi s.a.